SPORTY KIDS

TENNIS

COLLECT ALL THE SPORTY KIDS!

Joe is awesome at footy.
So why is handballing
so hard?

Emma is a swimming
superstar. But can she
learn to dive?

Jessica is a basketball
all-star. So why can't
she play without her
lucky shoes?

Luca never loses on the
handball court. But can
he beat the school's
Handball King?

Abby always wins
at soccer. So why won't
Pete join her team?

FELICE ARENA

ILLUSTRATED BY **TOM JELLETT**

SPORTY KIDS

TENNIS

PUFFIN BOOKS

PUFFIN BOOKS

UK | USA | Canada | Ireland | Australia
India | New Zealand | South Africa | China

Penguin Books is part of the Penguin Random House group of companies
whose addresses can be found at global.penguinrandomhouse.com.

Penguin
Random House
Australia

First published by Penguin Group (Australia), 2015

Design by Tony Palmer © Penguin Group (Australia)
Typeset in 18pt New Century Schoolbook
Colour separation by Splitting Image Colour Studio, Clayton, Victoria
Printed and bound in Australia by Griffin Press,
an accredited ISO AS/NZS 14001
Environmental Management Systems printer.

National Library of Australia Cataloguing-in-Publication data:
Arena, Felice, author.
Sporty kids: tennis/Felice Arena with
illustrations by Tom Jellett.

ISBN 978 0 14 330844 7

Other Authors/Contributors: Jellett, Tom, illustrator.

A823.3

MIX
Paper from
responsible sources
FSC® C009448

puffin.com.au

CHAPTER ONE

Stefan loved tennis. He
knew everything about it.
Each afternoon he practised
his shots. He hit a tennis
ball against the back wall
of his house.

Thoomp! Whoomp!
Boomp! Stefan liked the
sounds it made. It was
almost like a drumbeat.

Thoomp went the ball
as it made contact with
the racquet. *Whoomp* went
the ball when it hit the
wall. *Boomp* went the ball
when it bounced off the
pavement.

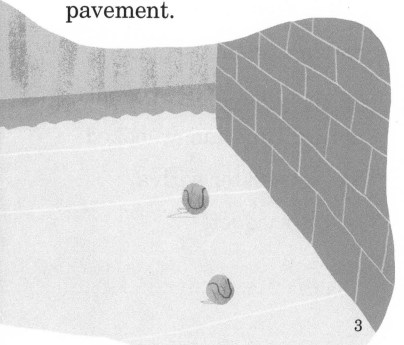

Stefan played every day after school.

When the sun was setting, the shadow of the big tree in the backyard flickered across the wall.

It looked as if Stefan was playing against someone – but not just another tennis player. The shadow looked like a monster with a tennis racquet!

It was a different
monster every time.

Stefan called them the
Grand Slam Beasts. Today
he was playing against the
Smashing Demon.

'So it's the Australian Open Final,' Stefan said, tapping the ball up and down on his racquet. 'And you think you can crush me? Really? Well then, bring it on, beast!'

CHAPTER TWO

Stefan knew that with
a name like Smashing
Demon, this beast would
be great at hitting the ball
hard, right into the middle
of the court.

He had to stop the beast playing its favourite shot – the smash.

Stefan served.

The Smashing Demon returned with a super-fast shot. It was impossible to hit the ball back.

The Smashing Demon looked pretty happy about that.

11

How could Stefan stop
the Demon from hitting a
smash?

This time, he tapped the
ball, low and gentle.

The Demon ran in too
late and missed.

'Yes!' Hitting the ball softly meant that the Demon couldn't return with a big smash.

The next couple of shots
dropped short on Stefan's
side of the court.

He returned them easily.

The Smashing Demon
was furious! It was also a
majorly sore loser.

It began shooting fireballs
from its bottom and kicking
over the drink stations.

'RAAAARRRR!' growled
the beast, before exploding
into a giant black puff of
smoke.

17

18

'Woo-hoo!' Stefan cheered.
'Take that, fire butt!'

'Who are you talking to?'
came a voice.

Stefan turned around and
saw a girl looking over the
fence.

CHAPTER THREE

'I'm Emma,' said the girl.
'We just moved in here.
I think we're going to the
same school.' She looked
around the yard. 'So...who
are you talking to?'

'No one,' said Stefan, feeling embarrassed.

'Yes, you were,' said Emma. 'Was it that monster on the wall? Because he looked really angry.'

Stefan smiled. 'It was,' he said. 'That's a Grand Slam Beast and I just beat it in the Australian Open Final.'

'Cool!' said Emma. 'I love games like that. I'm coming over.'

Emma disappeared behind the fence.

Before Stefan could say 'Grand Slam', she came running through the side gate.

'So who's your next opponent?' she asked.

23

The afternoon sun had dipped some more and the shadow on the wall had changed its shape.

'It's the Lobbing Lizard,' said Stefan. 'And I'm about to play against him in the Wimbledon Final.'

'Wimbledon is a big tennis tournament in England,' he explained.

'Cool,' said Emma. 'I'm going to be the Queen of England.' She made her voice sound very posh.

'In the name of the Queen, I order you to beat that beast!'

'Yes, Your Highness,' said Stefan. 'One royal butt-kicking coming right up.'

CHAPTER FOUR

The Lobbing Lizard was
a mean-looking beast. It
started with its best move,
the lob. It hit the ball really
high and deep into the
court.

The ball spun over
Stefan's head. He couldn't
run back in time to return it.

But for the next shot
Stefan had a plan.

'If that's the only trick
you've got,' he said, 'then,
take this!'

Stefan ran backwards,
just as the beast hit the
ball.

He got under the shot
and returned it.
WHAAAACKK!

Stefan smashed the ball
right into the middle of the
wall.

34

It was an awesome
return. The Lobbing
Lizard couldn't even get its
racquet to the ball.

Queen Emma cheered.
'Great shot!'

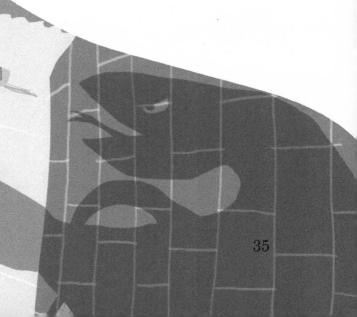

For the rest of the game the scaly beast repeated his jaw-dropping lob shots. And each time Stefan got into position and smashed them into winning points for himself.

Thoomp! Whoomp! Boomp!

The Lobbing Lizard
hissed at him. It began to
smash its racquet.

'Yes!' yelled Stefan, throwing his arms in the air. 'Game, set and match to me. I'm the Wimbledon champion!'

CHAPTER FIVE

'Nice one!' said Emma. 'Can I have a go?'

'Really?' said Stefan. 'Can you play tennis?'

'Yeah,' said Emma, picking up Stefan's racquet.

'I play all the time.
My mum's been teaching
me. But I really want to
play a Grand Slam Beast.'

'You do?' said Stefan. 'Are
you ready to take on the
meanest beast of them all –
the Rally Robot? In the US
Open Final?'

Emma grinned. 'Oh, yeah,' she said, bouncing the ball ready to serve.

It was almost dark and the shadow on the wall had doubled in size.

'Let's do it,' Emma said.

The Rally Robot was
a super tennis player. It
could do everything! It had
a mean serve, an amazing
backhand and a sizzling
forehand.

It was awesome at rallies.

Emma served.

The Rally Robot hit a
powerful return.

Emma ran for the ball
and hit it back, right into
the middle of the wall.

The Rally Robot made the
shot, but so did Emma.

'Wow,' said Stefan.

'You're really good!'

The ball went back and forth. It looked like Emma and the Robot were evenly matched. But then the Rally Robot tapped a shot just over the net.

Emma ran in but she couldn't get to the ball in time.

'Oh no!' said Stefan.

One point to the Robot!

CHAPTER SIX

Stefan's heart was racing.
It was the best tennis battle
he had ever seen. Well, the
best he'd seen in his backyard.

Emma began to hit
different shots.

She hit one low and
short, and the next high
and long.

The Rally Robot had to run around the court.

It began to buzz and crackle – it was losing its cool. It punched its giant steel fists into the court.

'Nice one!' said Stefan.
'You're confusing the bolts
out of that old rust bucket!'
Emma grinned and
served again.

She won the next three
points...then the match.

And the Rally Robot just
fell apart.

'Woo-hoo!' yelled Stefan.
'That was awesome.'

'Thanks,' said Emma.
'You're pretty awesome too.'

'Emma!' cried a voice
from over the fence.
'Dinner's ready!'

'That's Mum. I've gotta
go,' said Emma.

'Really? Already?' Stefan
sighed. 'Are you sure?'

He'd never had this much
fun playing on his own.

'Yeah,' said Emma. 'It's getting dark. But maybe we could play tennis tomorrow.'

'Yes!' said Stefan. 'The beasts won't know what hit them! Wait till you face the Backhand Blob.'

57

But Emma shook her
head. 'No, not against the
beasts,' she said.

'You and me. I'll bring my racquet and we can play against each other.'

'Tennis is even more fun when you have someone else to play with,' said Emma.

Stefan couldn't stop smiling.

READ THE BOOKS AND MEET THE SPORTY KIDS...

Abby Walsh

Abby loves to win, especially at soccer. It's her favourite sport and she's the star of the team. She's got the skills to take on anyone!

Angus is fast, clever and knows everything there is to know about Aussie Rules. He's awesome in attack – the footy team's top goal-scorer.

Angus Chung

Ben Jakande

Ben is a fan of everything sporty. He knows all the players, all the stats and every sporting record there is. He's a walking, talking wikipedia of sport!

Emma is creative and loves acting almost as much as sport. She's a great all-rounder with an original way of looking at every sporting situation.

Emma Ashworth

Jacqui can tell you who to play in what position, and which tactics to use – she's the brains behind any team. Need a winning strategy? Ask Jacqui!

Jacqui Abraham

Jessica Ito

Jessica is the smallest in the class, but she's also the star of the basketball team. She won't brag about it, though – she thinks she's just very very lucky!

Joe is funny, cheeky and loves team sports. He's a terrific all-rounder and a natural at almost everything, so he's keen to give anything a try.

Lizzie is the heart of any team. She's the commentator, scorer and cheer squad, all rolled into one. No one loves sport more than Lizzie!

Luca is super strong and super confident, like his twin sister, Sofia. He's a natural leader and the king of the handball courts at lunch.

Luca Farelli

Lucy Ka

Lucy is the fastest kid in class. She's not so keen on playing team sports – but she's super fit and the queen of the athletics track.

Oliver is bigger and stronger than anyone else in class. His favourite sport is swimming. He's not so good at losing – but that's because he usually wins!

Oliver Petersson

Pete Karim

Pete is the ultimate team player, but he also loves to win. He knows how to bring a team together to get the best out of everyone.

Sofia Forelli

Sofia is lots of fun and is super competitive, like her twin brother, Luca. She's awesome at sport, especially ball sports, and she's always the first picked for any team.

Stefan Rivera

Stefan is imaginative and very independent so he loves individual sports like tennis. Give him a sporting skill to learn and he's all over it!

EMMA'S MUM'S TIPS ON HITTING A FOREHAND!

You can practise your tennis skills, like Stefan does, by playing against a wall or with a ball on a string. But once you learn to hit the ball, there's nothing better than playing with a friend.

The forehand is the basic stroke in tennis. Once you can hit a forehand, you can learn how to control where the ball goes, how fast it's travelling, even how it spins!

Here's how to hit a forehand:

- Start with the racquet out in front of you with the edge up.
- Bring your arm back and turn your body to the side – but always keep your eyes on the ball!
- Swing in a straight line with the strings aiming at the ball.
- Don't stop when you hit the ball – follow through with your racquet.

Other tennis skills include the backhand, the smash and the lob. So practise your forehand, then grab your mum or dad and have a rally!

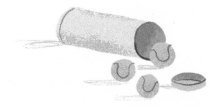

STEFAN'S FAVOURITE TENNIS JOKES!

Why is tennis such a noisy game?
*Because everyone makes such
a racquet.*

Did you hear about the sale on
tennis balls?
It's first come, first serve.

This one is for your parents:
What time does Sean Connery
arrive at Wimbledon?
Tennish!

What do you serve but don't eat?
A tennis ball!

What do you call someone who lies
across the middle of the court?
Annette!

Knock! Knock!
Who's there?
Tennis
Tennis who?
Tenn-is five plus five.

Why can't fish play tennis?
*They don't like getting close to
the net.*

What did one tennis ball say to the
other tennis ball?
See you round!

STEFAN'S AWESOME TENNIS FACTS!

Did you know?

- At first tennis was played by hitting the ball with your hand. Racquets have been used since the 16th century.
- The most important tennis tournaments are known as Majors or Grand Slams.
- The Grand Slams are the Australian Open, Wimbledon, the French Open and the US Open.

- Wimbledon is the only Grand Slam played on grass.
- Sabine Lisicki has the fastest recorded serve in the women's game. The men's record is held by an Australian, Samuel Groth.
- Margaret Smith Court holds the record for the most Grand Slam single titles – she won 24 titles.
- Some of the greatest tennis champions have come from Australia – including Rod Laver, Margaret Court, John Newcombe and Yvonne Goolagong Cawley.
- In 1932, Henry Austin was the first to wear shorts at Wimbledon. Before that, players wore trousers, skirts and even jumpers!

FELICE SAYS...
I love tennis. Tennis means long, lazy summer days watching the Australian Open on the telly – and me excitedly jumping on the couch and shouting every time my favourite player makes an awesome shot. It also means me trying to figure out how to hit the same shots on the tennis court the next day!

TOM SAYS...
One of the best things about tennis has to be the sounds. The *squeep* of tennis shoes on the court, the *doink* of the ball hitting the sweet spot on the racquet and, best of all, the *pssshpt* of a new can of tennis balls being opened.